monday morning®

# Let's Learn About
# WORDS

bed

car

dog

egg

by Marilynn G. Barr

BOYS & GIRLS LIBRARY
WESTFIELD ATHENAEUM
WESTFIELD, MA 01085

MAY 0 8 REC'D

D1200733

_____

Name

## has learned all about
# Words.

_____   _____
Date                                    Teacher

MM2231
LET'S LEARN ABOUT WORDS
Entire contents copyright © 2007 by Monday Morning Books, Inc.

Production: Little Acorn & Associates, Inc.

For a complete catalog, write to the address below:
Monday Morning Books, Inc.
PO Box 1134
Inverness, CA 94937

Call our toll-free number: 1-800-255-6049
E-mail us at: MMBooks@aol.com
Visit our Web site: http://www.mondaymorningbooks.com for fun freebies.
Visit our Blog: http://mondaymorningbooks.blogspot.com

Monday Morning® and the Monday Morning sun logo are
registered trademarks of Monday Morning Books, Inc.

Permission is granted to the individual purchaser to reproduce designated student materials in this book for non-commercial individual or classroom use. The purchase of this book does not entitle reproduction of any part for an entire school, district, or school system. Such use is strictly prohibited.

No part of this publication may be reproduced or transmitted in any form or by any means, electronic or mechanical, including photocopying, scanning, recording, or storing in any information storage and retrieval system or electronic online bulletin board, without prior permission from Monday Morning Books, Inc.

ISBN 1-57612-235-2

Printed in the United States of America
9 8 7 6 5 4 3 2 1

WESTFIELD ATHENAEUM
WESTFIELD, MASS. 01085

Let's Learn About Words

# Contents

J 372.21
BAR

# Introduction

Children learn first words with four adorable critters (a butterfly, bumble bee, bird, and worm) found in *Let's Learn About Words*. This title features five activity formats. Youngsters practice identifying beginning sounds, trace first words, cut and paste beginning sound letters, and make personalized word pockets and first words mobiles.

Little ones practice identifying letters on flower and leaf wreaths, then color matching pictures on activity sheets found in I Can Color Beginning Sound Pictures.

I Can Trace First Words activity sheets feature pre-k and kindergarten first words for children to trace, then color matching pictures.

Youngsters make My First Words books with completed activity sheets found in I Can Cut and Paste Beginning Sound Letters.

Reproduce oak tag Critter Word Pockets for children to color, cut out, and assemble. Children place word cards in personalized critter pockets as they learn new words, including sight words.

A Butterfly Named ... features a cover, writing page, and mobile patterns for children to make writing practice booklets or first words mobiles.

## Puppet Patterns

Reproduce, color, and cut out puppet patterns. Program each pattern with a beginning or ending sound letter. Glue a craft stick to the back of each puppet cutout. Allow each child to choose a puppet. Invite each child, in turn, to share a word that begins or ends with the letter on his or her puppet.

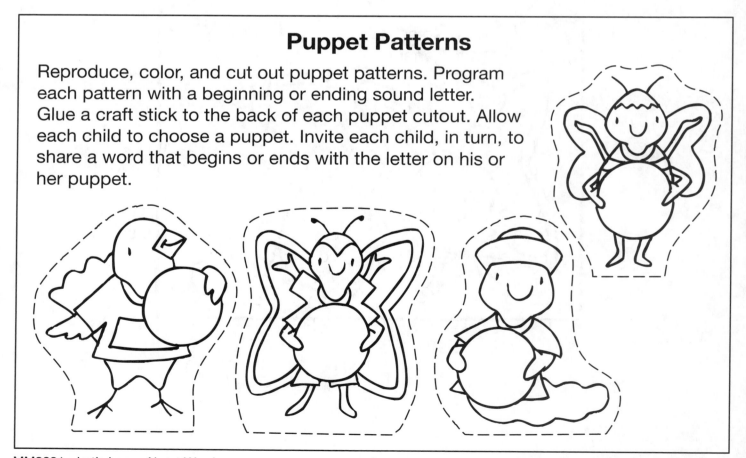

 © 2007 Monday Morning Books, Inc.

# I Can Color Beginning Sound Pictures

Little ones practice identifying letters on flower and leaf wreaths, then color matching pictures on activity sheets found in I Can Color Beginning Sound Pictures.

Reproduce activity sheets for children to color and cut out. Children can cut out completed activity sheets along the dotted lines to make a standard book, or cut out the circles. To make a round book, measure and cut round construction paper sheets.

## Materials:

Construction paper, crayons, scissors, glue, hole punch, yarn, brass fasteners

## Directions:

### Standard Book

1. Provide each child with a construction paper cover to decorate.
2. Help each child glue his or her completed activity sheets on construction paper.
3. With the cover on top, stack the pages in order.
4. Punch three holes along the left side of the cover and on each page.
5. Lace and tie yarn through each hole to form a book.

### Round Book

1. Provide each child with a round construction paper cover to decorate.
2. Help each child glue his or her completed activity sheets on round construction paper.
3. With the cover on top, stack the pages in order.
4. Punch a hole at the top of the cover and on each page.
5. Fasten the cover and pages with a brass fastener.

I can color pictures that begin with letter **b**.

Look at the pictures.

Circle the pictures that begin with the letter **b**.

Color the rest of the picture.

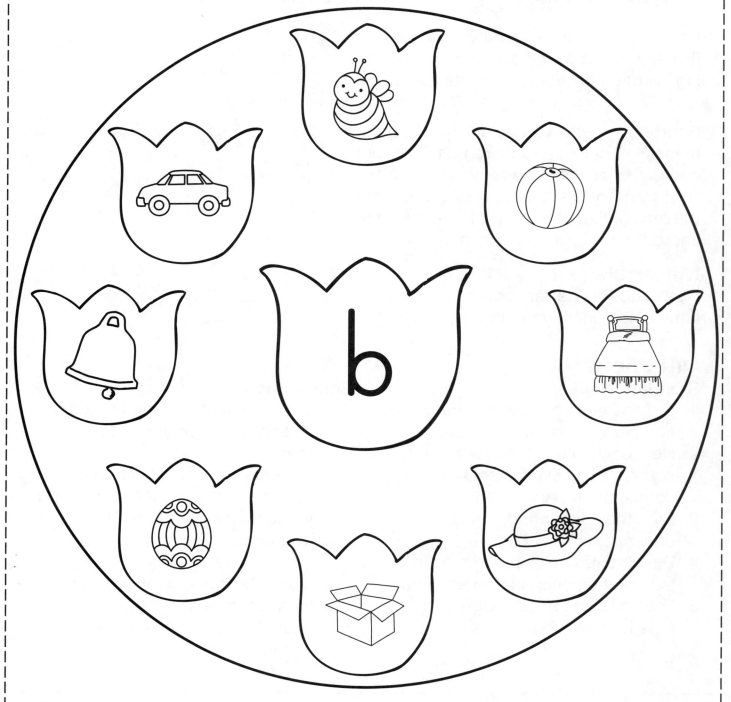

# I can color pictures that begin with letter c.

Look at the pictures.

Circle the pictures that begin with the letter c.

Color the rest of the picture.

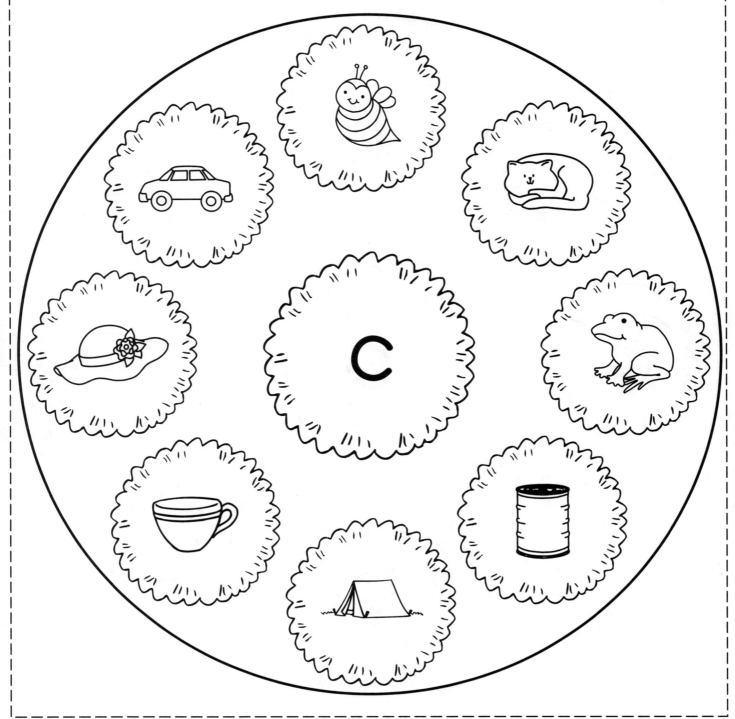

# I can color pictures that begin with letter d.

Look at the pictures.

Circle the pictures that begin with the letter **d**.

Color the rest of the picture.

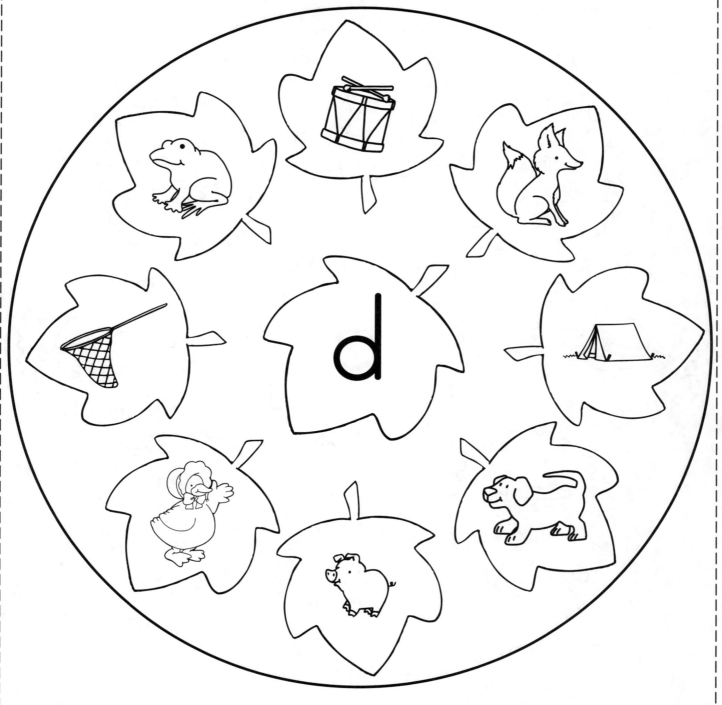

8 © 2007 Monday Morning Books, Inc.

Provide crayons and scissors.

I can color pictures that begin with letter **f**.

Look at the pictures.

Circle the pictures that begin with the letter **f**.

Color the rest of the picture.

# I can color pictures that begin with letter h.
Look at the pictures.

Circle the pictures that begin with the letter h.

Color the rest of the picture.

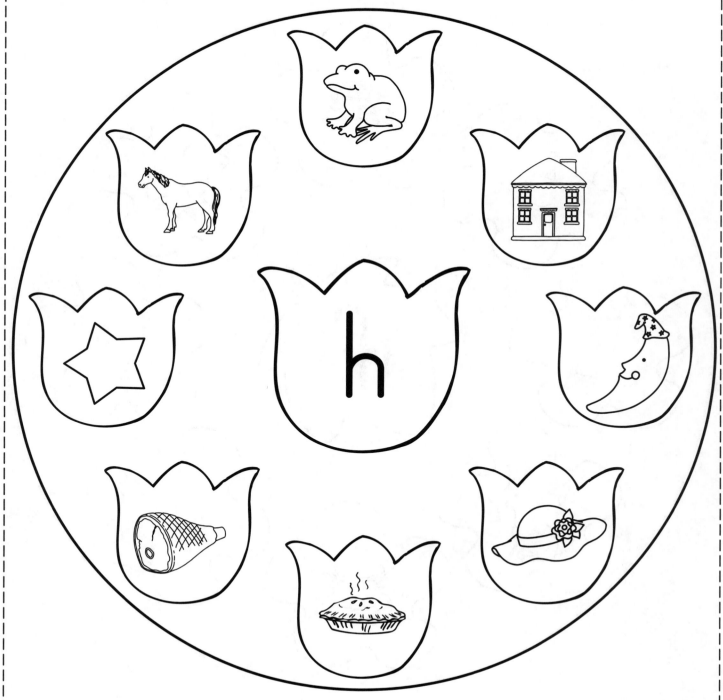

**10**

© 2007 Monday Morning Books, Inc.

Provide crayons and scissors.

# I can color pictures that begin with letter m.

Look at the pictures.

Circle the pictures that begin with the letter m.

Color the rest of the picture.

# I can color pictures that begin with letter n.

Look at the pictures.

Circle the pictures that begin with the letter n.

Color the rest of the picture.

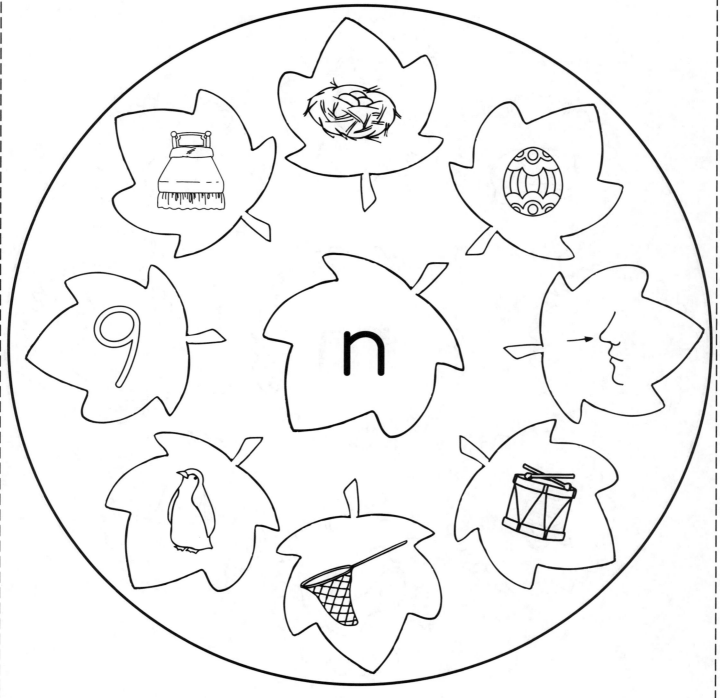

**12** © 2007 Monday Morning Books, Inc.

I can color pictures that begin with letter p.
Look at the pictures.
Circle the pictures that begin with the letter p.
Color the rest of the picture.

13  © 2007 Monday Morning Books, Inc.

# I can color pictures that begin with letter s.

Look at the pictures.

Circle the pictures that begin with the letter **s**.

Color the rest of the picture.

# I can color pictures that begin with letter t.

Look at the pictures.

Circle the pictures that begin with the letter t.

Color the rest of the picture.

**15**

© 2007 Monday Morning Books, Inc.

# I Can Trace and Match First Words

These activity sheets feature pre-k and kindergarten first words for children to trace, then color matching pictures.

Reproduce activity sheets for children to color, cut out, and make first word practice books.

## Materials:
Construction paper, crayons, scissors, glue, hole punch, yarn

## Directions:
1. Provide each child with a construction paper cover to decorate.
2. Help each child glue his or her completed activity sheets on construction paper.
3. Stack the pages in order.
4. Punch three holes along the left side of the cover and on each page.
5. Lace and tie yarn through each hole to form a book.

Provide crayons and scissors.

# I can trace and match words.

Trace the letters.

Circle the picture that matches each word.

Color the rest of the picture.

**17**

© 2007 Monday Morning Books, Inc.

# I can trace and match words.

Trace the letters.

Circle the picture that matches each word.

Color the rest of the picture.

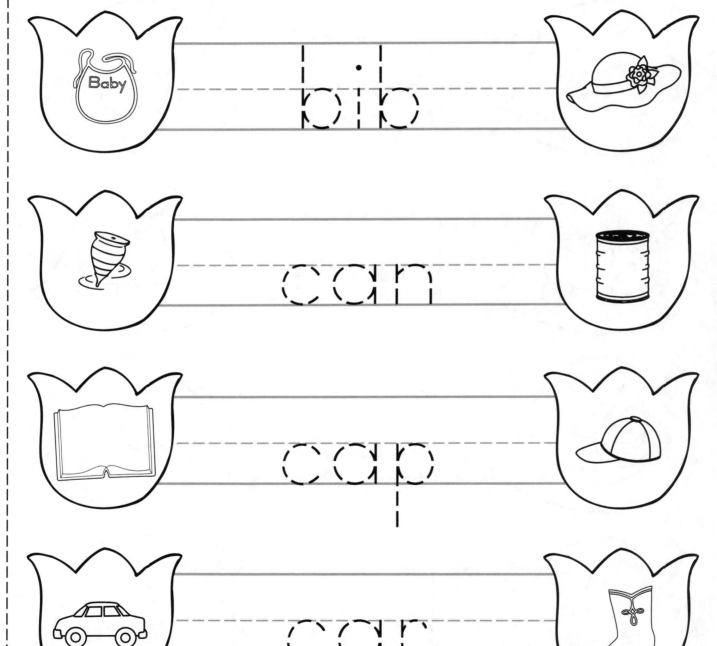

bib

can

cap

car

18  © 2007 Monday Morning Books, Inc.

I can trace and match words.

Trace the letters.

Circle the picture that matches each word.

Color the rest of the picture.

cat

cow

cup

dog

# I can trace and match words.

Trace the letters.

Circle the picture that matches each word.

Color the rest of the picture.

egg

fan

fox

hat

© 2007 Monday Morning Books, Inc.

Provide crayons and scissors.

# I can trace and match words.

Trace the letters.

Circle the picture that matches each word.

Color the rest of the picture.

ice

jar

key

net

I can trace and match words.

Trace the letters.

Circle the picture that matches each word.

Color the rest of the picture.

one  1

pan

pig

pot

 © 2007 Monday Morning Books, Inc.

I can trace and match words.
Trace the letters.
Circle the picture that matches each word.
Color the rest of the picture.

23

© 2007 Monday Morning Books, Inc.

I can trace and match words.
Trace the letters.
Circle the picture that matches each word.
Color the rest of the picture.

two

2

van

web

wig

© 2007 Monday Morning Books, Inc.

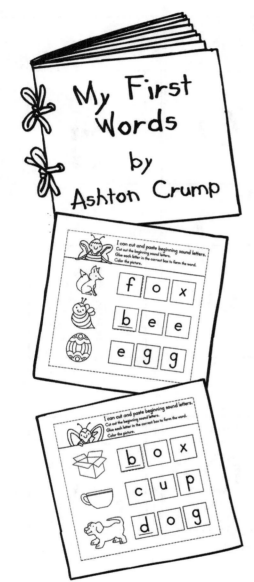

# I Can Cut and Paste Beginning Sound Letters

Youngsters make My First Words books with completed activity sheets found in I Can Cut and Paste Beginning Sound Letters.

Reproduce activity sheets for children to color, cut out, and make first word practice books.

Measure and cut construction paper sheets slightly larger than a finished activity sheet cutout.

## Materials:

Construction paper, crayons, scissors, glue, hole punch, yarn

## Directions:

1. Provide each child with a construction paper cover to decorate.
2. Help each child glue his or her completed activity sheets on construction paper.
3. Stack the pages in order.
4. Punch two holes along the left side of the cover and on each page.
5. Lace and tie yarn through each hole to form a book.

# I can cut and paste beginning sound letters.

Cut out the beginning sound letters.

Glue each letter in the correct box to form the word.

Color the picture.

 | o | g

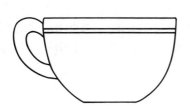

 | u | p

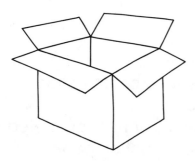

 | o | x

c | b | d

© 2007 Monday Morning Books, Inc.

Provide crayons and scissors.

# I can cut and paste beginning sound letters.

Cut out the beginning sound letters.

Glue each letter in the correct box to form the word.

Color the picture.

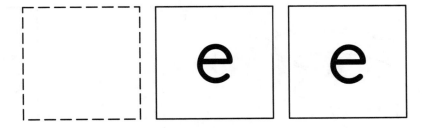

o x

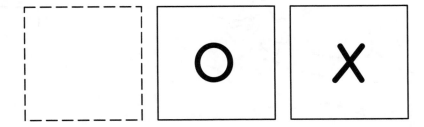

e e

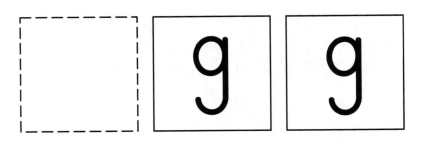

g g

b f e

© 2007 Monday Morning Books, Inc.

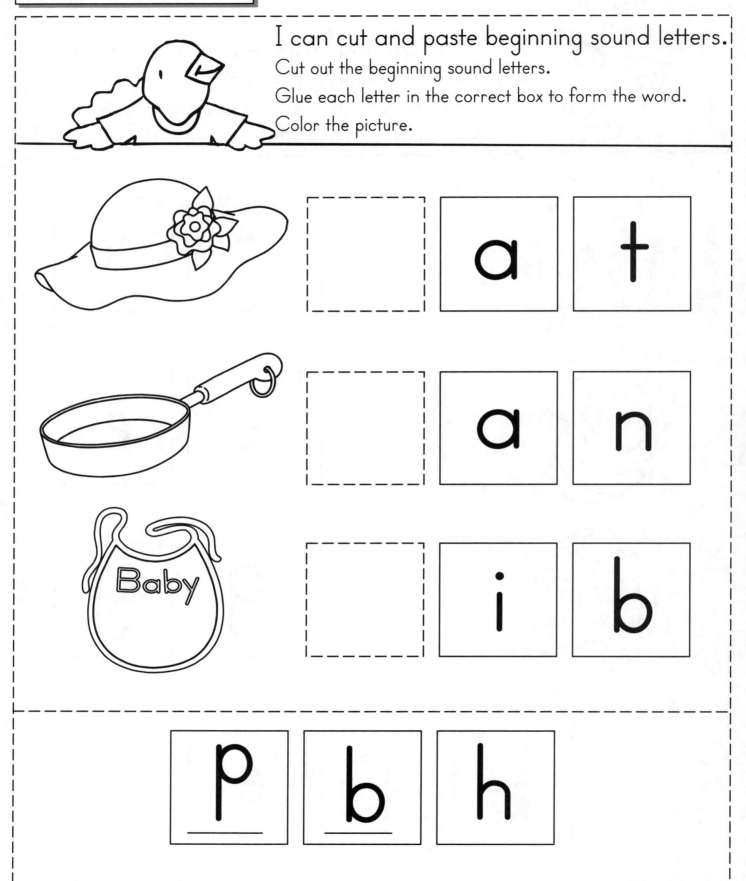

I can cut and paste beginning sound letters.
Cut out the beginning sound letters.
Glue each letter in the correct box to form the word.
Color the picture.

28

© 2007 Monday Morning Books, Inc.

# I can cut and paste beginning sound letters.

Cut out the beginning sound letters.
Glue each letter in the correct box to form the word.
Color the picture.

 | | e | d

 | | a | n

 | | i | g

v | p | b

# I can cut and paste beginning sound letters.

Cut out the beginning sound letters.

Glue each letter in the correct box to form the word.

Color the picture.

e n

a r

a t

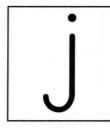 

t j b

**30**    © 2007 Monday Morning Books, Inc.

# I can cut and paste beginning sound letters.
Cut out the beginning sound letters.
Glue each letter in the correct box to form the word.
Color the picture.

| | c | e |
|---|---|---|

| | e | t |
|---|---|---|

| | o | w |
|---|---|---|

| i | n | c |
|---|---|---|

**31**   © 2007 Monday Morning Books, Inc.

I can cut and paste beginning sound letters.
Cut out the beginning sound letters.
Glue each letter in the correct box to form the word.
Color the picture.

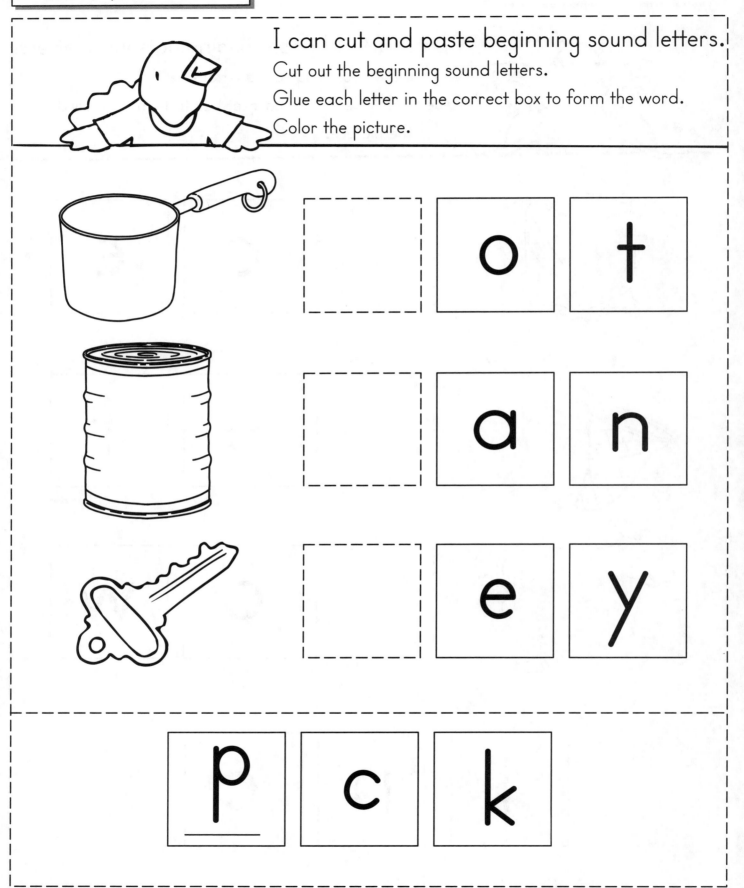

32     © 2007 Monday Morning Books, Inc.

# I can cut and paste beginning sound letters.
Cut out the beginning sound letters.
Glue each letter in the correct box to form the word.
Color the picture.

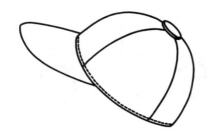

| s | c | w |

 I can cut and paste beginning sound letters.
Cut out the beginning sound letters.
Glue each letter in the correct box to form the word.
Color the picture.

34   © 2007 Monday Morning Books, Inc.

Provide crayons and scissors.

I can cut and paste beginning sound letters.
Cut out the beginning sound letters.
Glue each letter in the correct box to form the word.
Color the picture.

1  [ ] n  e

  [ ] a  n

2  [ ] w  o

o  f  t

# I can cut and paste beginning sound letters.

Cut out the beginning sound letters.

Glue each letter in the correct box to form the word.

Color the picture.

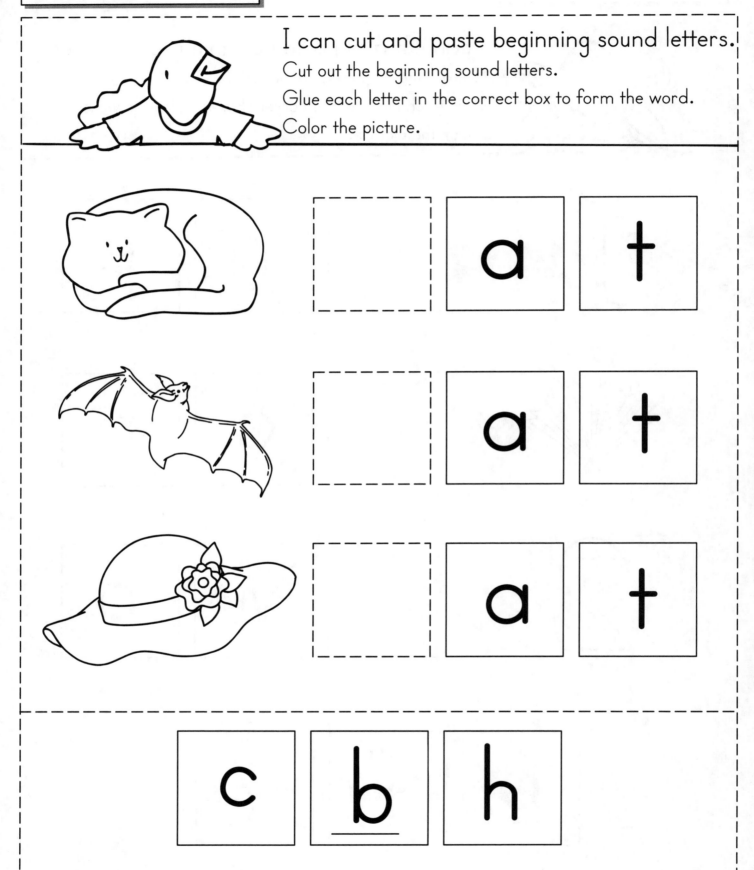

| | a | t |
| | a | t |
| | a | t |

| c | b | h |

Provide crayons and scissors.

# I can cut and paste beginning sound letters.

Cut out the beginning sound letters.

Glue each letter in the correct box to form the word.

Color the picture.

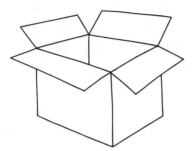   

o x

i x

o x

b s f

# Critter Word Pockets

Reproduce oak tag Critter Word Pockets for children to color, cut out, and assemble. Children place word cards in personalized critter pockets as they learn new words.

## Materials:
Construction paper, crayons, scissors, tape, hole punch, yarn

## Directions:
1. Have children color and cut out their critters and pockets.
2. Attach the pocket on each child's critter with tape along the bottom and sides.
3. Help children write their names on their critters.
4. Punch a hole at the top of each critter.
5. Lace and tie yarn through the hole to form a hanger.
6. Hang each child's Critter Word Pocket on a display board.
7. Program, reproduce, cut apart, and place word cards in a box near the display board.
8. Designate a time for children to take turns drawing and reading a word card.
9. If correct, the child may put the card in his or her Critter Pocket. If incorrect, the child returns the card to the box.
10. Reproduce additional cards as needed.

Provide crayons, scissors, and tape.

# Critter Word Pocket

Color and cut out the butterfly and pocket.
Use tape to attach the pocket to the butterfly.
Place word cards in the pocket.

**Pocket**

Attach the
pocket here.

**39**

© 2007 Monday Morning Books, Inc.

Provide crayons, scissors, and tape.

# Critter Word Pocket

Color and cut out the bee and pocket.
Use tape to attach the pocket to the bee.
Place word cards in the pocket.

Attach the
pocket here.

**Pocket**

40     © 2007 Monday Morning Books, Inc.

Provide crayons, scissors, and tape.

# Critter Word Pocket

Color and cut out the worm and pocket.
Use tape to attach the pocket to the worm.
Place word cards in the pocket.

**Pocket**

Attach the
pocket here.

41

© 2007 Monday Morning Books, Inc.

Provide crayons, scissors, and tape.

# Critter Word Pocket

Color and cut out the bird and pocket.
Use tape to attach the pocket to the bird.
Place word cards in the pocket.

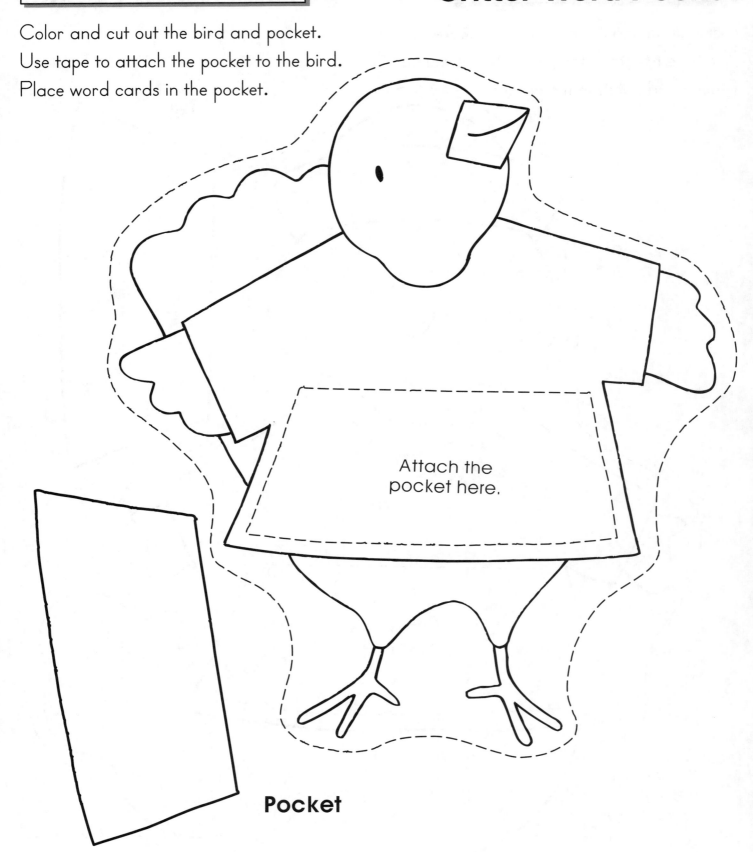

Attach the
pocket here.

**Pocket**

# A Butterfly Named ...

Reproduce oak tag butterfly covers and six writing pages for each child to make a booklet to practice writing words in class or at home.

Reproduce and cut out mobile patterns for children to make first words mobiles.

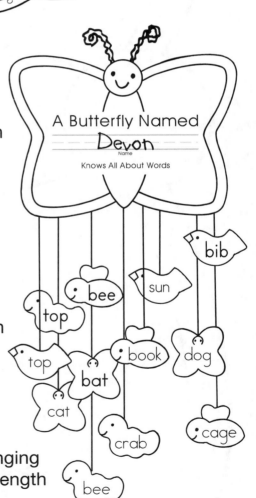

## Materials:

Construction paper, crayons, scissors, tape, pipe cleaners, hole punch

## Directions:

### Writing Practice Booklet

1. Have children color and cut out their butterfly cover patterns.
2. Help children glue on pipe cleaner antennae then write their names on the covers.
3. Punch two holes on the left side of each cover cutout and writing pages.
4. Cut, lace, and tie a length of yarn through each set of holes to form a booklet.

### First Words Mobile

1. Have children color and cut out their butterfly cover patterns.
2. Help children glue on pipe cleaner antennae then write their names on the cover cutouts.
3. Cut and tape different lengths of yarn to the back of the butterfly cutout.
4. Help each child write mastered words on mobile cutouts.
5. Tape each programmed mobile cutout to the hanging yarn. Note: Tape more than one cutout on each length of yarn.

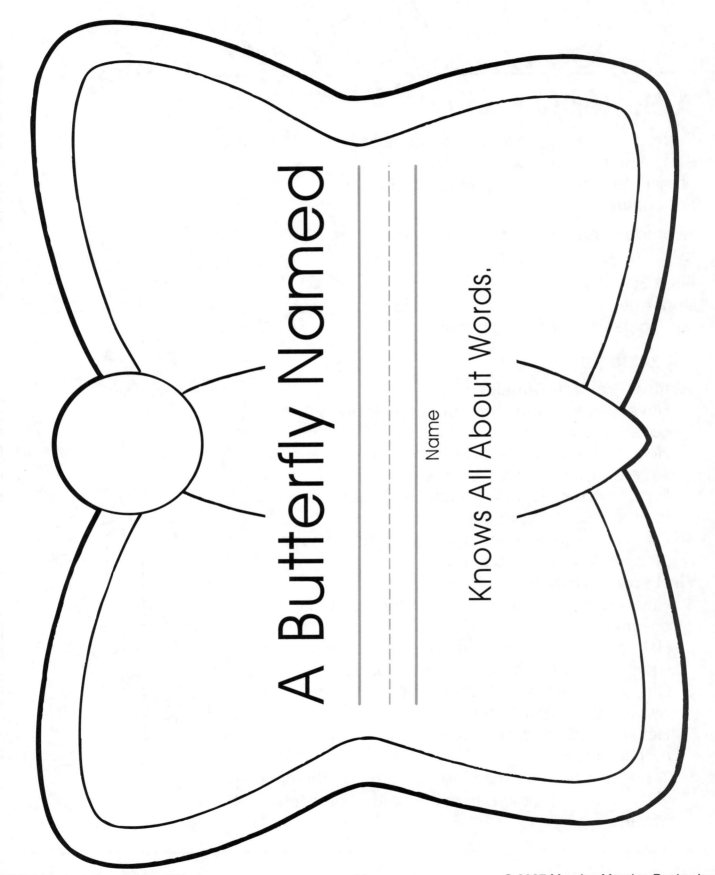

A Butterfly Named

Name

Knows All About Words.

44

© 2007 Monday Morning Books, Inc.

Provide crayons, scissors, and tape.

# Butterfly Writing Page

**45**

© 2007 Monday Morning Books, Inc.

# Mobile Patterns

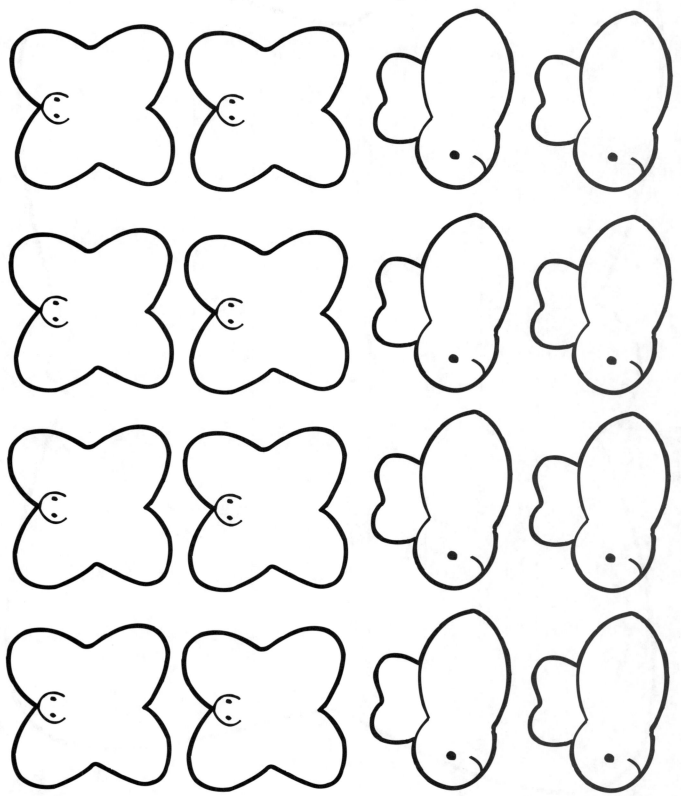

**47**

© 2007 Monday Morning Books, Inc.

# Sight Words

| | | | | |
|---|---|---|---|---|
| a | down | in | one | they |
| all | eat | into | our | these |
| am | find | is | out | too |
| and | five | it | play | two |
| are | for | jump | please | under |
| at | four | like | ran | up |
| ate | funny | little | run | we |
| away | go | look | said | well |
| be | glue | make | saw | went |
| big | has | me | say | what |
| but | have | must | see | who |
| came | he | my | she | will |
| can | her | new | so | with |
| color | hers | nine | soon | yes |
| come | his | no | that | you |
| cut | hot | not | the | |
| did | I | now | them | |
| do | if | on | there | |